A SUMMARY OF THE LAKE OF SOULS:

SEEKING TO OVERCOME THE LOSS OF HIS MENTOR, MR. CREPSLEY, DARREN JOINS HIS FRIEND HARKAT ON A TRIP TO A WORLD OF MONSTERS THROUGH MR. TINY'S MAGIC. DARREN AND HARKAT JOURNEY THROUGH THIS WORLD UNTIL THEY REACH THE LAKE OF SOULS, WHERE THEY LEARN THAT IN HIS FORMER LIFE, HARKAT WAS KURDA SMAHLT. OFFERING THEIR FAREWELLS TO KURDA, DARREN AND HARKAT RETURN HOME, WHERE THEY ARE SHOCKED TO LEARN THAT THIS ALTER-NATE WORLD WAS SIMPLY THE FUTURE, LONG AFTER THE WAR OF THE SCARS HAS CONCLUDED...

LORD OF THE SHADOWS
CONTENTS

BUT WHO IS THE "MONSTER" WHO STANDS TO INHERIT IT?

ME?

FACE ME ON THE GROUND, YOU MONSTER! FIGHT ME NOW!!

THIS WORLD BELONGS TO THE LORD OF THE SHADOWS NOW...

OR YOU?

AAH!

THANKS, HARKAT. MAYBE I WILL...

YOU CAN TELL ME... ABOUT IT, DARREN. I KNOW A LITTLE SOMETHING ABOUT... NIGHTMARES.

I'LL BE... FINE.

YOU'RE DRENCHED IN SWEAT. ANOTHER NIGHTMARE?

GEHO (COFF)

HI...

HI...

GEHO

DARREN! ARE YOU ALL RIGHT?

HA HA.

HAA (HUFF)

HAA

CHAPTER 95: HOMETOWN

ISN'T HE ON STAND-BY?

PACHI PACHI
(CLAP)

HEY, WHERE'S RHAMUS?

Coming up next, the man with two stomachs! The hungriest human in history, Rhamus Twobellies!!

OF COURSE THEY DID.

PAN
(SMACK)

GERTHA, ALEXANDER, THEY LOVED YOU!!

MUSHA
(MUNCH)

MUSHA

!!

THERE REALLY IS NO LIMIT TO HOW MUCH HE CAN EAT...

GOOOO

BUT I'M SO HUNGRY...

HURRY!

DON'T EAT BEFORE YOU GO ON STAGE, RHAMUS! YOU NEED ROOM FOR THE SHOW!

WHAT'S UP?

PARTS OF ME STILL CAN'T BELIEVE THIS PIECE OF INFORMATION...

HARKAT HAD BEEN KURDA IN HIS FORMER LIFE.

...WE RETURNED TO THE CIRQUE DU FREAK TO WORK AS HANDYMEN.

AFTER FINISHING UP OUR QUEST TO DISCOVER HARKAT'S FORMER IDENTITY...

JUST ADMIRING YOUR... HANDSOME LOOKS!

I MEAN, THE ONLY THING THEY SHARE IN COMMON IS THE FACIAL SCARS...

NIGORI (SMIRK)

SOUNDS LIKE YOU'VE FINALLY LEARNED TO APPRECIATE TRUE CHARACTER, DARREN.

GOSHI (RUB)

GOSHI

BUT BY REGAINING THE MEMORY OF HIS FORMER LIFE, HARKAT KEEPS THAT PIECE OF KURDA ALIVE WITHIN HIM...

AT LEAST, THAT'S WHAT I WANT TO BELIEVE.

...BY RETURNING TO THE LAKE OF SOULS, RATHER THAN TAKE HIS PLACE.

KURDA CHOSE TO LEAVE HARKAT ALIVE...

BUT I CAN'T JUST HIDE IN THE CIRQUE DU FREAK FOREVER.

I NEED TO RETURN TO VAMPIRE MOUNTAIN ...

MR. TALL CLAIMED THERE WAS NO DEVELOPMENT IN THE WAR OF THE SCARS...

SFX: LITO (NOD)

SO THAT'S IT FOR THIS TOWN. TOMORROW WE'LL BE OFF...

WHERE ARE YOU NOW... STEVE...?

SUU... (ZZZ)

ZA GZZZO ZA ZA ZA

A WAVE OF RED ON THE HORIZON ...

GOGOGO (RUMBLE)

MY THROAT IS BURN-ING.

WHERE AM I !!?

Y-YEAH, RIGHT...

TA CHOP)

LET'S GO, DARREN! THAT BOY NEEDS HIS... PRESENTS!

TRUSKA! I NEARLY FORGOT!

TIME FOR SHANCUS'S BIRTHDAY PARTY TO BEGIN.

DARREN, HARKAT! HERE YOU ARE!

...

HURRY!

I CAN'T TELL HIM THAT I MIGHT TURN OUT TO BE THE LORD OF THE SHADOWS...

...OR THAT I'VE BEEN HAVING THE SAME NIGHTMARE EVERY NIGHT...

HAPPY BIRTHDAY, SHANCUS!!!

CHEERS!!

HE'S SCALY AND HE'S GREAT, TODAY HE HAS TURNED EIGHT, HIS NAME IS SHANCUS! HAPPY BIRTHDAY!!

HIS NAME IS SHANCUS! HAPPY BIRTHDAY!!

HE'S LEAN, HE'S GREEN, SNOT HE'S NEVER SEEN...

I TOLD YOU TO THANK THE OTHERS FIRST!

HEY! SHAN-CUS!

BIRI (CRIPP)

BIRI

WOW! WHAT'S THIS ONE GONNA BE?

BYU (ZIP)

WHOA!

NO YOU DIDN'T!!

BUT I DID!

HA HA HA!

HEY! NO DODGING!

KYU (SCRIBBLE)

YOU'RE SO LUCKY!!

WOW, NEAT!! A NEW SNAKE!!!

PACHI (CLAP)

PACHI

PACHI

THANKS, UNCLE DARREN!!

URCHA...

DON'T TELL THE OTHERS.

PON (PAT)

BEING A FATHER SOUNDS HARD.

HE LOOKS MORE LIKE HIS MOTHER THAN ME, AND HE FEELS LIKE HE'S THE ODD ONE OUT.

URCHA'S THE ONLY KID OF OURS WITHOUT SCALES.

S-SORRY... I FORGOT VAMPIRES CAN'T HAVE KIDS.

DON'T WORRY ABOUT IT.

...!!

OH.

YOU'LL FIND OUT YOURSELF ONCE—

HARD? IT'S THE MOST FUN IN THE WORLD!

I'M JEALOUS, EVRA. I REALLY AM.

HA HA HA!

HANKS, MR. TALL!

HAPPY BIRTHDAY, SHANCUS.

AND TO ROUND OUT SHANCUS'S BIRTHDAY, MR. TALL WOULD LIKE TO ANNOUNCE OUR NEXT DESTINATION!

I'M HAPPY TO ANNOUNCE THAT OUR PERFORMANCES IN THIS TOWN WERE A SMASH SUCCESS!

YOUR WORK IS APPRECIATED.

YOU WERE ALL EXCELLENT.

OHHH!

NOW, AS FOR OUR NEXT DESTINATION...

PARARA (FLIP)

PIKU (TWITCH)

HAVEN'T BEEN THERE BUT THE ONE TIME, YEARS AGO...

AHH, THAT ONE!

?

THIS IS WHERE WE ARE NOW.

AND THIS...

...IS WHERE WE WILL BE GOING NEXT.

WHAT WILL YOU DO, DARREN?

YES, THAT WAS WHERE DAR-REN...

OH, I SEE...

?

YOU CAN TAKE A DIFFERENT ROUTE AND MEET UP WITH US LATER, IF YOU WISH.

YOU DON'T HAVE TO COME WITH US, DARREN.

...

DOES THAT TOWN MEAN SOME-THING, DARREN?

THAT'S THE TOWN...

...WHERE I WAS BORN.

TA
(TMP)

CHAPTER 96:
FAMILY

WOW, THIS BOOK-STORE IS STILL HERE!

BUN...
(VMM)

THERE WEREN'T THIS MANY CARS BEFORE.

THE TOWN'S REALLY CHANGED.

THIS IS WHERE ALAN AND I CAME TO BUY COMICS.

I WONDER IF ALAN AND TOMMY STILL LIVE HERE...

HA!

HA!

WHERE ARE THEY ALL NOW?

THE VIDEO ARCADE, WHERE STEVE AND I HUNG OUT.

TOMMY AND I HAD A LEGENDARY SHOOT-OUT ON THIS FIELD.

24

GUYS...

GOOD-BYE.

GOOD-BYE, TEACH-ER!

GOOD-BYE.

MR. DALTON!!

THAT'S MR. DALTON. HE'S THINNER THAN I REMEMBER, BUT THAT'S HIM!

MY FAVORITE TEACHER!!

AS FAR AS THEY KNOW, I DIED YEARS AGO. IF I RUN INTO PEOPLE I KNOW, IT WILL CAUSE PROBLEMS.

AND NOT JUST THAT...

I NEED TO CONTROL MYSELF HERE.

THAT WAS A CLOSE CALL, THOUGH.

...ALL OVER THE TV AND PAPERS AT THE TIME.

THEY SPLASHED MY NAME AND PHOTO...

I WAS ALSO ACCUSED OF MURDER IN MR. CREPSLEY'S TOWN. DON'T FORGET THAT.

DARREN SHAN, SERIAL MURDERER!!

MR. CREPSLEY'S HOME WAS IN A DIFFERENT COUNTRY, BUT IT WAS QUITE A BLOODY STRING OF EVENTS...

IT'S QUITE POSSIBLE THAT THEY REPORTED ON IT HERE.

EXCUSE ME, I'D LIKE TO LOOK AT THE LAST THREE YEARS' WORTH OF NATIONAL AND LOCAL NEWSPAPERS.

I NEED TO DO SOME RE- SEARCH...

OUR LIBRARY HAS CUT-DOWN VERSIONS OF THE NATIONAL PAPERS, AND THE LOCAL NEWS IS ON MICROFILM.

FOR A SCHOOL REPORT, IS IT? GOOD TO SEE A YOUNG MAN SO STUDIOUS.

FUU... (SIGH)

DOESN'T SEEM LIKE THE STORY ATTRACTED MUCH ATTENTION HERE...

Torres to the r

!?

I FEEL CON- FLICTED ABOUT THIS. YES, IT'S A RELIEF...

...BUT THEY DON'T SEEM TO CARE ABOUT WHAT HAP- PENED.

WAIT, THEY DON'T MEAN... *THAT* TOMMY, DO THEY!?

S-SORRY...

TOMMY JONES MAKES A SERIES OF UNBELIEVABLE SAVES...

...AND SOON SIGNED A FIVE-YEAR CONTRACT WITH A WORLD-FAMOUS FOREIGN TEAM.

HE'S NOW THE STARTING GOALKEEPER OF THE BEST CLUB IN THE COUNTRY.

...TOMMY JOINED A LOCAL PROFESSIONAL TEAM...

AFTER WORKING HIS WAY UP THROUGH THE AMATEUR RANKS...

TOMMY JONES, GREATEST KEEPER IN THE WORLD!!

BRILLIANT! A PRO SOCCER PLAYER!!

...AND THE MATCH IS AT THE STADIUM IN THIS TOWN!?

IT'S NEARLY UPON US!!

TOMMY'S TEAM IS IN THE SEMI-FINALS OF THIS YEAR'S TOURNAMENT...

... DARREN SHAN DIED YEARS AGO.

AS FAR AS THIS TOWN KNOWS ...

NOBODY NEEDS TO KNOW THAT ONE OF A PAIR OF FRIENDS IS NOW A LOCAL HERO, WHILE THE OTHER IS WANTED FOR MURDER...

I'M GLAD I DIDN'T FIND MY OWN NAME IN ANY ARTICLES ...

NOW I WANT TO KNOW ABOUT MY FAMILY!

OUR OLD HOUSE ...

ANNIE !!

MOM, DAD!

MAY I HELP YOU!?

...BURSTING OUT OF THE DOOR ON THE WAY TO SCHOOL...

I CAN PRACTICALLY SEE ANNIE...

GACHA (CLICK)

IT'S LIKE THE HOUSE HAS BEEN STUCK IN TIME...

IT HASN'T CHANGED... SAME COLOR DOOR, SAME STYLE CURTAINS... IT'S ALL THE SAME!

DO

DO (THUMP)

AT WHAT, PRE- CISELY?

J- JUST LOOK- ING.

Jl...
(STARE)

THEY STILL MIGHT. I'M NOT SURE...

W- WELL...MY COUSINS LIVED HERE. IN FACT...

OH ...

DERMOT AND ANGELA MOVED AWAY THREE OR FOUR YEARS AGO.

YOU'RE RELATED TO ANNIE?

DAD... MOM...

YES...AND DERMOT AND ANGELA. DO THEY STILL LIVE HERE?

I RE-MEMBER MY DAD SAYING SOME-THING...

YOU KNOW ABOUT THAT?

...

NOT SINCE THEIR BOY DIED.

THEY SHOULD HAVE LEFT SOONER.

IT WAS NEVER A HAPPY HOUSE.

THE FAMILY STAYED ON, BUT IT WAS A MISERABLE PLACE AFTER THAT.

HE FELL OUT OF A WINDOW.

...

PECHA
(BLAH)

ペ チャ

クチャ

KUCHA
(BLAH)

I WASN'T LIVING HERE THEN, BUT I'VE HEARD ALL ABOUT IT.

WHAT ABOUT ANNIE?

DID SHE GO WITH THEM?

OH, NO...

HEART ATTACK! IS HE OKAY?

YES, DERMOT HAD A MILD HEART ATTACK. FORCED HIM TO RETIRE EARLY...

HAA
(WHEW)

I SAID IT WAS MILD, DIDN'T I?

RE-TIRED...

THEY DECIDED TO MOVE WHEN DERMOT RETIRED. LEFT FOR THE COAST.

HER SON.

BOY?

SHE STILL LIVES HERE— HER AND HER BOY.

ANNIE STAYED.

I'VE LIVED ABROAD MOST OF MY LIFE.

OH...

YOU DON'T SEEM TO KNOW MUCH ABOUT YOUR OWN FAMILY.

ARE YOU SURE YOU'RE A RELATIVE?

WHAT DO YOU MEAN?

THE BOY'S A NICE ENOUGH CHILD, BUT HE'S NOT REALLY A SHAN...

THEN I GUESS YOU'RE OLD ENOUGH.

WHAT'S SHE GOING ON ABOUT?

UH... SIX-TEEN...

ACTUALLY, I SUPPOSE IT'S NOT THE SORT OF THING YOU TALK ABOUT IN FRONT OF CHILDREN. HOW OLD ARE YOU?

HE WAS BORN OUT OF WEDLOCK.

ANNIE WAS ON THE YOUNG SIDE.

JUST SWEET SIXTEEN WHEN THE BABY WAS BORN!

AHA HA HA!

IRA (IRK)

I GUESS LOTS OF WOMEN CHOOSE NOT TO MARRY THESE DAYS...

TRUE, BUT...

SFX: GU (CLENCH)

I'M NOT EVEN SURE ANYONE EXCEPT HER KNOWS WHO THE FATHER IS.

ANNIE NEVER MARRIED.

WHAT A WAY TO REPAY A GOOD STORY...

HMPH!

...

OH, BUT THERE'S MORE...

I SEE. THANKS FOR THE STORY.

WHY THROW YOUR LIFE AWAY SO YOUNG?

IT'S NOT AS IF I WANT TO MEET THEM AND DO SOMETHING ABOUT IT.

JUST CATCH A GLIMPSE TO SEE IF THEY'RE DOING ALL RIGHT...

I'VE PUT EVERYONE THROUGH HELL...

ANNIE, A MOTHER? HARD TO BELIEVE...

GABA (CLICK)

THIS IS STUPID. WHAT AM I DOING?

I NEED TO GO BACK TO THE CIRQUE...

OOH,
IT'S
COLD...

I WANT TO GRAB HER, TO HUG HER...

I WANT TO CALL OUT TO HER.

JA (SCRAPE)

...TO LET HER KNOW I'M RIGHT HERE!

ANNIE!!!

PIKU (TWITCH)

MOM! I'M HOME!!

TATA (CHOP)

WAIT A SEC...

SORRY.

I THOUGHT I TOLD YOU TO BRING IN THE CLOTHES.

ABOUT TIME!

DOTATA (STOMP)

BATAN (SLAM)

DO YOU WANT ME TO TAKE SOME OF THOSE?

MY LITTLE HERO.

NOW COME IN. IT'S COLD OUTSIDE.

AS LONG AS YOU'RE HAPPY WITH YOUR LIFE...

OH, ANNIE... I'M SO GLAD.

THAT'S ALL I WANTED TO KNOW ...

CHAPTER 97:
DARIUS

SO, YOUR PARENTS... MOVED OUT OF THIS TOWN...

TIME TO FEED THE... LITTLE PEOPLE!!

DARREN!

IT'S HARD NOT TO CRY WHEN YOU WITNESS THE ENORMITY OF WHAT YOU SET IN MOTION...

...

KOSO (SNEAK)

GUZU... (SNIFF.)

HUH?

YOU LOOK LIKE YOU CRIED A LOT LAST NIGHT.

I FORGOT THAT MAKES HIM MY NEPHEW. I'M AN UNCLE!

NEPHEW! I JUST THOUGHT OF HIM AS ANNIE'S SON.

GA

WHAT ABOUT YOUR NEPHEW? ANY FAMILY RESEMBLANCE?

GA (CHOMP)

AAAH!!

DOSHA (CL'LINK)

GARA (CLOMP)

GURA (FLOP)

HANDSOME, OF COURSE, LIKE ALL THE SHANS.

JI... (PEER)

A NICE KID, FROM WHAT I SAW.

OF COURSE.

A... BOY?

HANG ON! HE'S NOT FOOD.

WARA

WARA (STOMP)

AAAHH!!!

CAN YOU STAND?

BA (CLAP)

...

DARIUS.

HE LOOKS ABOUT ANNIE'S SON'S AGE.

HI, I'M HARKAT.

I'M DARREN.

THEY SAID IT WASN'T SUITABLE FOR CHILDREN.

I TRIED BUYING A TICKET, BUT NOBODY WILL SELL ME ONE.

THIS IS THE FREAK SHOW, ISN'T IT?

WHY DON'T YOU WALK AROUND WITH US? IF YOU STILL WANT A TICKET, MAYBE WE CAN SORT ONE OUT FOR YOU THEN.

HA-HA-HA! TELL YOU WHAT.

MUSU (SULK)

THAT'S WHY I WANT TO SEE IT.

IT IS A BIT ON THE GRUESOME SIDE.

YES, WELL...

OR YOURSELF... AT HIS AGE?

DOES HE MAKE YOU THINK ABOUT... YOUR NEPHEW?

BOYS ARE CURIOUS AT THAT AGE.

YOU SURE, DARREN?

WHAT THE HELL, I'VE NOTHING BETTER TO DO.

HMM... A BIT OF BOTH, I GUESS.

YES, MASTER.

COME ON! I'M READY!

I HOPE HE'S ENJOYING HIMSELF.

HE DOESN'T SEEM ALL THAT INTERESTED...

JI
(STARE)

FUNNY KID...

COME ON, STICK CLOSE SO YOU DON'T GET LOST.

I'M FINE...

AHH...

I WANT THE CIRQUE TO BE MY OWN SECRET.

I GUESS. MY FRIEND OGGY'S TOO CHICKEN, AND HE'S GOT A BIG MOUTH.

DID YOU COME HERE BY YOUR-SELF?

...IF THE TWO OF US DECIDE...

GOSO
(RUSTLE)

MOZO
(RUSTLE)

OF COURSE, IF NOBODY KNOWS YOU'RE HERE, THEN THEY WON'T FIND OUT...

DAR-REN...

HEE HEE!

MAYBE I'LL SCARE HIM A LITTLE BIT.

L-LEAVE ME ALONE !!!

GASHA (CLUNK)

...TO GOBBLE YOU UP!!!

BIKU (TWITCH)

I'M NOT GOING TO HURT YOU.

EASY, EASY ...

I JUST DON'T LIKE PEOPLE SAYING STUFF LIKE THAT.

IT'S NOT FUNNY ...

HAA (CHUFF)

HAA

... CREATURES LIKE YOU MAKING THREATS LIKE THAT.

I DIDN'T MEAN IT...

COURTESY OF THE HOUSE!

WELL, IF IT'S FREE.

HOW ABOUT I GET A TICKET TO TONIGHT'S SHOW FOR YOU, TO MAKE UP FOR SCARING YOU?

...

SU— (SWISH)

HMM...

A TICKET?

CHILDREN TEND TO FARE UN-FAVORABLY AT THE CIRQUE DU FREAK.

PA (FLICK)

Cirque du Freak

WEST STAND LOWER
ROW:25 SEAT:0007

YOURSELF, STEVE LEONARD, SAM GREST.

BE CAREFUL, DARREN. DO NOT BE RASH ...

THANKS MR. TALL!!

GI CREAK)

Cir que du freak

...

YOUR DECISIONS HAVE SET A TRAIN OF EVENTS IN MOTION.

THINK CARE-FULLY ...

DON'T BE LATE TO THE SHOW.

THAT'S OKAY, THEN.

OF COURSE !!

HUH ?

DARIUS, HOW WOULD YOU FEEL ABOUT JOINING THE CIRQUE DU FREAK?

HERE YOU GO.

NOT WITH YOU CREEPS !!

BA GNATCHJ

YOU DON'T WANT TO TRAVEL AROUND THE WORLD?

I DON'T MEAN THAT.

HE WAS A BIT SULLEN, BUT LOTS OF KIDS HIS AGE ARE LIKE THAT.

I WAS THAT WAY MYSELF WHEN I FIRST JOINED THE CIRQUE.

I DON'T LIKE HIM.

A STRANGE KID.

...CREATURES LIKE YOU MAKING THREATS LIKE THAT.

I'M QUITE OBVIOUSLY NOT HUMAN.

BUT...

...?

YOU DIDN'T PICK UP ON IT? WHEN HE ACCUSED US OF THREATENING HIM...

SO? WE AREN'T NORMAL.

HE SAID, "CREATURES LIKE YOU."

WHAT TIPPED HIM OFF TO THE FACT...

...THAT YOU AREN'T EITHER?

DARI-
US...

BUT UNLESS WE CAN FIND DARIUS AND QUESTION HIM...

IT'S QUITE POSSIBLE.

I DON'T THINK THE VAMPANEZE WOULD RECRUIT CHILDREN, BUT STEVE, ON THE OTHER HAND...

WAA CRAHH

OR MAYBE WE'RE JUST OVER-THINKING THIS...

PERHAPS HE COULD TELL... WE WERE ONTO HIM.

...AND DARIUS NEVER SHOWED.

THE SHOW'S OVER...

BEEN A WHILE... HASN'T IT?

D...

DARREN... SHAN...

...SO WITH THE HELP OF MY PARENTS, I FAKED MY DEATH AND JOINED THE CIRQUE.

THE CIRQUE DU FREAK MIGHT PRESENT A WAY TO HEAL MY CONDITION...

AS I DID WITH DEBBIE, I SPUN HIM A TALE ABOUT A RARE DISEASE THAT SLOWED MY BODY'S DEVELOPMENT.

AFTER A LONG, HEAVY SILENCE, I BEGAN TO SLOWLY TELL HIM MY STORY.

...BUT THERE WAS NO WAY I COULD TELL HIM THE TRUTH.

IT WAS A PAINFUL CHOICE...

THINK OF THE TERRIBLE PAIN SHE'S BEEN THROUGH...

AND TO KEEP IT A SECRET FROM ANNIE, YOUR OWN SISTER...

BUT THERE MUST HAVE BEEN SOME OTHER WAY.

HOW WOULD WE HAVE EXPLAINED IT? THE CIRQUE DU FREAK IS AN ILLEGAL TRAVELING SHOW.

WHY WOULD YOU PUT EVERYONE THROUGH SO MUCH PAIN?

YOU FAKED YOUR OWN DEATH?

I STILL REGRET THE EFFECTS TODAY...

IT WAS A HORRIBLE DECISION TO HAVE TO MAKE...

...

...

YOU REMEMBER ALAN?

GOT TWO KIDS TOO.

I'VE MANAGED ALL RIGHT BY MYSELF.

A STAR KEEPER?

YOU'VE GOT QUITE A CAREER FOR YOURSELF.

BUT WHAT ABOUT YOU?

HA HA!

AS LONG AS YOU DON'T CLONE YOUR-SELF! ONE ALAN IS ENOUGH!

YEAH! I TOLD HIM...

REALLY? ALAN?

BIG INTO CLONING.

HE'S A GENETICIST— QUITE A FAMOUS ONE!

...

SO I SUPPOSE... YOU DON'T KNOW WHAT HAPPENED TO STEVE.

WHAT DID STEVE DO?

HE GOT INTO SOME TROUBLE THE LAST TIME HE WAS HERE... YOU REALLY HAVEN'T HEARD?

I'VE ONLY SEEN HIM ONCE SINCE THEN, ABOUT TEN YEARS AGO. HE RETURNED HOME FOR A FEW MONTHS WHEN HIS MOTHER DIED.

HE LEFT HOME AT SIXTEEN. RAN OFF WITHOUT A WORD TO ANYONE.

IT'S OLD HISTORY. BEST NOT TO BRING IT UP.

EY!!

MOZO (TWIST)

OH, I DON'T RIGHTLY REMEM-BER...

PLUS, I GOT TO SEE YOU AGAIN.

I'D WANTED TO SEE IT EVER SINCE I MISSED MY CHANCE WHEN WE WERE KIDS.

I REALLY ENJOYED THE SHOW.

OH DAMN, WHAT'S THE TIME?

BA (ZIP)

THAT'S OKAY ...

SORRY, DARREN! I REALLY HAVE TO GO!

DORURUN (VRRM)

WE MUST TALK SOME MORE...

THANKS, TOMMY.

I'LL SEND YOU A TICKET IN THE MORNING.

REALLY? I'D LOVE TO.

HEY, HOW'D YOU LIKE TO COME SEE ME PLAY TOMORROW?

I'LL SEE YOU AFTER THE GAME.

WE'LL TALK ABOUT IT TOMORROW. IT MIGHT HELP YOU MAKE UP YOUR MIND ABOUT SOME OTHER THINGS.

T-TOMMY...

THERE ARE THINGS YOU SHOULD KNOW. I DON'T WANT TO GET INTO THEM NOW—IT'S TOO LATE—BUT I THINK...

...ABOUT STEVE...

SEE YOU TOMOR-ROW.

WHAT DOES HE WANT TO TELL ME ABOUT STEVE...?

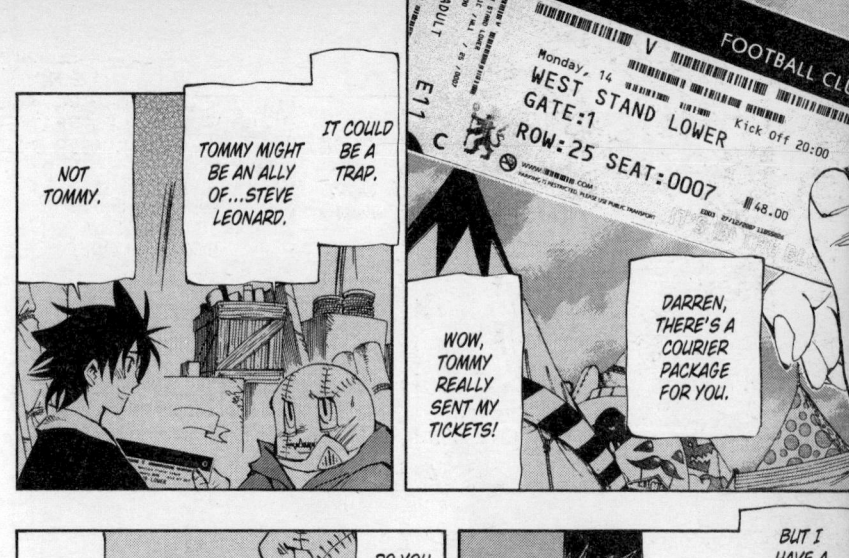

NOT TOMMY.

TOMMY MIGHT BE AN ALLY OF...STEVE LEONARD.

IT COULD BE A TRAP.

WOW, TOMMY REALLY SENT MY TICKETS!

DARREN, THERE'S A COURIER PACKAGE FOR YOU.

HA-HA, YOU WOULDN'T BE ABLE TO GET IN.

DO YOU WANT ME TO COME... WITH YOU?

THERE ARE THINGS YOU SHOULD KNOW.

...OR SET US ON HIS TRAIL.

BUT I HAVE A FEELING HE MIGHT IN SOME WAY BE ABLE TO DIRECT US TO HIM...

......

...IN A CROWD LIKE THAT, I'LL BE PERFECTLY SAFE!

BESIDES, HARKAT...

WOW!

THEY JUST LOVE TOMMY!

IT'S NOT UNUSUAL, HE'S THE GREATEST NUMBER ONE!

IT'S NOT UNUSUAL IF THE OTHER TEAM SCORES NONE!

NOW, WHERE'S MY SEAT...?

PII (FWEET)

WAA (RAHH)

THERE ARE THE PLAYERS!

WE'RE ABOUT TO BEGIN!

SCRAM, IF YOU VALUE YOUR LIFE!!

OUTTA THE WAY!

TOMMY.

TOMMY.

TOMMY!!

TOMMY...

KYAA (AAHHH)

WAA (AAHH)

BURU

BURU (SHIVER)

HOW COULD STEVE STRIKE LIKE THIS, IN FRONT OF SUCH AN ENORMOUS CROWD!?

TO BE SO CRUEL AND BRAZEN, RIGHT BEFORE MY EYES...

AAAAH HHHHH !!!!!•••••

AND TOMMY, OF ALL PEOPLE!!!

FOLLOW THE SMELL OF TOMMY'S BLOOD!

DON'T LOSE THE TRAIL!!

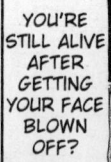

YOU'RE STILL ALIVE AFTER GETTING YOUR FACE BLOWN OFF?

THAT VOICE... MORGAN JAMES.

DAR-RUHN...

DARRUHN HYUHN...

JA...
(SCRAPE)

...

HELLO, GANNEN. STILL HANGING OUT WITH MADMEN AND SCUM, I SEE.

ARE YOU REALLY ALL THAT MAD THAT TOMMY DIED?

YOU'RE LIKE A RAGING BEAST.

OH, THE LOOK ON YOUR FACE, DARREN...

A SPY? DON'T GET THE WRONG IDEA, DARREN...

DARIUS IS AN EXCEPTION.

HAVE YOU NO SHAME?

DARIUS... SO HARKAT WAS RIGHT.

HAVE YOU STARTED BLOODING CHILDREN TO BE YOUR SPIES NOW, STEVE?

YES, OF COURSE.

C-CAN I REALLY SHOOT HIM?

OKAY ...

I DON'T WANT TO HURT A CHILD.

DON'T DO IT, DARIUS. YOU CAN'T GO BACK AFTER THAT.

DARIUS, NO!!

THEN PULL THE TRIGGER.

BE STEADY AND AIM TRUE.

I'LL SHOOT HIM NOW, DAD!

CHAPTER 99: LAUGHINGSTOCK

D... DAD!?

CHAPTER 99:
LAUGHINGSTOCK

GUAA GAAAGH

AAAGH!!

UHH...

HEE HEE HEE HEE!

RIGHT WHERE I TRAINED YOU TO HIT HIM.

WELL DONE, SON.

(BAKI GCRACK)

GAAAHHH!!

WHAT'S GOING ON?

SON? DAD!?

HE IS AT OUR MERCY.

LET'S FINISH HIM OFF QUICKLY.

NIYANIYA (SMIRK)

BA
(LEAP)

MORGAN,
R.V.!!
FAN
OUT!!!

CAN'T...
FOCUS...

THE
PAIN IS
CLOUD-
ING MY
VISION!

GURA
(LURCH)

I JUST DIDN'T THINK IT WOULD BE SO...SO...

TAKE IT EASY. I WANT TO SEE DARREN SQUIRM SOME MORE...

REMEMBER, HE MUST DIE AT YOUR HAND!

FINISH HIM NOW! WHAT IF HE BLEEDS TO DEATH ON YOUR SON'S ARROW?

BLOODY? YES, BUT YOU DID GOOD WORK TONIGHT.

ARE YOU OKAY, DARIUS?

URP... ULG...

O... OKAY ...

STEP BACK, SON.

YOU DON'T HAVE TO WATCH THE REST IF YOU DON'T WANT TO.

A LONG, TWISTED STORY.

HOW DID... YOU END UP WITH...A SON?

LOOK FOR AN ESCAPE ROUTE!

BUY SOME TIME...

HAH.

OPTIMISTIC TO THE LAST.

...BEFORE I DRIVE A STAKE THROUGH YOUR HEART!

ONE I'LL DELIGHT IN TELLING YOU...

POTA (DRIP)
POTA

WRONG WAY ROUND... I'LL BE THE ONE DOING...THE KILLING TONIGHT.

I THINK I CAN CATCH THEM UNAWARE AND LEAP OVER THE WALL BEHIND ME!

WITH DIGNITY AND HONOR?

...HOW DID TOMMY DIE?

SPEAKING OF DYING...

OR LIKE THAT SQUEALING PIG CREPSLEY?

BUTSU
(SNAP)

DOGO
(KBOOM)

BAGI
(THWAM)

A WOUNDED BEAST IS THE MOST DANGEROUS KIND!

I WARNED YOU!

MUH LUHD!

AAAGH!!!

GARA
(CLUNK)

WAS THAT A FLIT... WITHOUT A WARM-UP?

SUCH NERVE FROM A MERE HALF-VAMPIRE...

ZEH
(WHEEZE)

ZEH

I'VE FELT THIS SENSATION BEFORE...

MY BODY FEELS LIKE IT'S ON FIRE! AND IT'S NOT JUST FROM THE PAIN...

CAN'T RUN STRAIGHT...

THE PAIN IS GETTING TO MY HEAD...

THUHR YUH ARRH!!

HEE'TH UVER HURR!!

JAKA
(CHK)

NO! STAY AWAY FROM THE WINDOW!

PA

PA
(FLICK)

WAS THAT A GUN- SHOT!?

-DAGO
(KBOOM)

YOU'RE BLEED- ING!

HEY, ARE YOU ALL RIGHT!?

ZAAA
(FSHHH)

GU
(TUG)

SU
(SWISH)

NO.
THIS
IS TOO
EASY.

TOO
FAST.

HEE!
HEE!
HEE!

I'LL DO
WHAT I
PLEASE
!!!

THIS IS THE
PREDICTED
FOURTH
ENCOUNTER!
YOU MUST
DO IT NOW,
BEFORE—

DON'T BE
FOOLISH!
YOU HAVE
TO KILL
HIM!

WHAT
OF THE
FATE OF
THE VAM-
PANEZE
!?

THEN
WHAT OF
MR. TINY'S
PROPHECY
!?

I KNOW
WHAT
I'M
DOING,
GANNEN.

I CAN'T
KILL HIM
THIS
WAY.

HAA
CHUFF?

THAT
MUG IN
THE RAIN
BOOTS
DOESN'T
RULE MY
LIFE!!!

STUFF
IT!

I'LL
CREATE
MY OWN
DESTINY!

WHAT THE HELL'S GOING ON DOWN THERE?

I'M CALLING THE POLICE !!

HA!

HA!

HA!

HA!

CATCH YOU LATER...

GU (SQUEEZE)

...VAMPIRE-GATOR...

FUAN

FUAN (WEEOOO)

HOW LOW...

...CAN YOU SINK...?

IF THEY LOOK UP MY IDENTITY AND FIND OUT I'M A WANTED MAN...

I CAN'T GET TAKEN TO THE POLICE OR THE HOSPITAL.

ZUZU (DRAG)

DAR-
REN.

HAA

HAA
(HUFF)

WHAT'S
HAPPENING
TO ME...?

MY
BODY...
BURNING
UP...

THAT
VOICE...
IS THAT
WHO I
THINK IT
IS?

DAR-
REN!

DEBBIE!?

DAR-
REN!
YOU'RE
AWAKE
!!

ALICE,
COME
HERE!

DAR-
REN'S
AWAKE!!

TAKE IT
EASY!
YOU'RE
REALLY
HURT...

ZUK!
(THROB)

AM I...
DREAM-
ING?

AM I
SEEING
THINGS?

AND ALICE? WHAT ARE YOU DOING HERE!?

HE IS!?

WELL DONE, DECLAN, KENNY.

TURNS OUT YOU SAVED A FRIEND OF THE LADIES!

DON'T WORRY, WE'RE ALL FRIENDS HERE.

OH...THEY CARRIED ME HERE.

...BUT THEY FINALLY AGREED TO ACCEPT OUR HELP.

IT WASN'T EASY TO CONVINCE YOUR VAMPIRE LEADERS...

...IN ORDER TO FIGHT BACK AGAINST THE VAMPETS.

REMEMBER WHAT WE SAID BEFORE? WE NEEDED TO ORGANIZE...

SO WHO ARE THESE PEOPLE?

THEY JUST INSIST ON CALLING US THAT...

LADIES OF THE SHADOWS...?

SO YOU CAN FOCUS ON THE WAR WITH THE VAMPANEZE!

WE'RE GONNA FIGHT AGAINST THE VAMPETS!

THE LADIES OF THE SHADOWS TAUGHT US THE WAY.

AN ARMY OF HUMANS ORGANIZED TO FIGHT BACK AGAINST THE VAMPETS.

VAMPIRITES!!

ARE YOU EVEN LISTENING TO ME!?

NOT ONLY DID YOU FAIL, HE NEARLY COULD HAVE KILLED YOU!

WHY DIDN'T YOU FINISH DARREN OFF?

MY LORD!!

OH, SHUT YOUR TRAP, GANNEN...

RIGHT, DARIUS?

CHAPTER 100: LADIES OF THE SHADOWS

WE'VE STILL GOT SOME SECRETS UP OUR SLEEVE...

LOOK, DON'T PUSH IT...

...THAT HE NEEDS TO KNOW.

CHAPTER 100:
LADIES OF THE SHADOWS

KARI
(SCRITCH)
KARI

KARI

GOOD MORNING TO YOU TOO, DEBBIE.

HEY, I TOLD YOU NO ACTIVITY! LIE BACK DOWN.

DAR-REN!!

COME ON IN.

BA (CLAP)

ANYWAY, YOU'VE GOT A GUEST.

I DO?

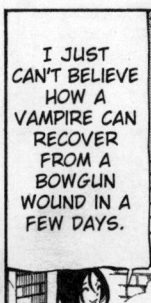

I JUST CAN'T BELIEVE HOW A VAMPIRE CAN RECOVER FROM A BOWGUN WOUND IN A FEW DAYS.

IT'S EVEN SHOCK-ING ME!

I'M HEALING FASTER BY THE MINUTE.

SO IT TURNS OUT DARIUS WAS CONNECTED TO STEVE, AFTER ALL...

BUT WHO WOULD HAVE GUESSED THEY WERE FATHER AND SON?

ARE YOU ANGRY OR HAPPY? MAKE UP YOUR MIND!

HAR- KAT !!

I'M SO GLAD YOU'RE ALIVE!!

I LEFT YOU AT THE SOCCER MATCH... AND THEN I DON'T HEAR FROM YOU IN DAYS!!

DO YOU HAVE ANY IDEA HOW WORRIED... I WAS?

THEY'RE A HUMAN FORCE WE ASSEMBLED TO FIGHT THE VAMPETS.

ABOUT THESE VAMPIR-ITES...

HEH HEH!

DECLAN AND KENNY, TWO OF THE VAMPIRITES, SAVED ME IN THE NICK OF TIME.

YOU LEAVE THOSE VAMPETS UP TO US!

...WE'RE ALSO NOT BOUND BY THE USUAL VAMPIRE RULES.

JUST AS THE VAMPETS CAN USE WEAPONS FREELY...

AND VANEZ WAS A BIG HELP IN TRAINING US IN HOW TO FIGHT WITH THE CREATURES OF THE NIGHT.

SEBA AND VANEZ HELPED US SELL THE IDEA.

I'M IMPRESSED THAT YOU CONVINCED THOSE HARD-HEADED VAMPIRE GENERALS TO ALLOW THIS!

YEAH! WE DON'T WANNA WATCH OUR OWN KIND FALL VICTIM ANY LONGER!

IT'S FOR OUR OWN SAKE AS WELL!

HEE HEE!

THEY MUST HAVE LIVES AND FAMILIES.

IT'S REAS-SURING TO KNOW THEY'RE ON OUR SIDE, BUT IS IT RIGHT TO INVOLVE THEM?

HOME-LESS!?

WHY—

THERE ARE POLICE-MEN AND SOLDIERS AMONG THE VAMPIRITES...

...BUT MOST ARE HOME-LESS.

YOUR OWN KIND?

THAT MEANS THERE ARE EVER MORE HUMANS FALLING VICTIM TO THEIR KIND.

...THE VAMPANEZE ARE BLOODING NEW MEMBERS EN MASSE.

SINCE THE VAMPIRES HAVE THE ADVANTAGE IN NUMBERS...

NOBODY'S GOING TO KEEP AN EYE ON THE HOMELESS POPULATION, NO MATTER WHAT HAPPENS...

SIMPLE: MAKE SURE MOST VICTIMS ARE UNTRACEABLE HOMELESS LIKE US.

HOW CAN THEY KEEP KILLING MORE AND MORE HUMANS WITHOUT IT BECOMING HEADLINE NEWS?

SO THEY'RE FIGHTING NOT FOR JUSTICE OR THE VAMPIRE CAUSE, BUT THEIR OWN LIVES.

IT ALL MAKES SENSE.

AND WHO SHOULD ARRIVE BLOODY AND BRUISED BUT YOU, DARREN!

WE ARRIVED IN THIS TOWN TWO WEEKS AGO.

OUR VAMPIRITES WERE REPORTING A STRONG VAMPANEZE PRESENCE IN THE AREA.

WE'RE ALL IN THIS TOGETHER NOW.

WE FIGHT TO SUR-VIVE.

OFF TO DO MY WATCH...

CAREFUL, MATE. CALL IF ANYTHING HAPPENS.

THE HEADACHE IS KILLING ME TOO...

MY WOUNDS ARE ALMOST FULLY HEALED, BUT THE FEVERISH SYMPTOMS WON'T GO AWAY...

TOMMY... I SAW YOU DIE BEFORE MY EYES, AND I COULDN'T DO A THING...

WHAT WAS IT HE WANTED TO TELL ME?

JONES

JUST HOW FAR WILL YOU SINK, STEVE?

HE KILLED HIS OWN FRIEND...

THE LORD OF THE SHADOWS...

...IS YOU.

IF I AM TO FIGHT A MONSTER...

...MUST I BECOME A MONSTER MYSELF?

URGH...

AAGH...

!

IT'S SO BRIGHT... MY HEAD IS SPLITTING!!

OOF!

DOSA (THUDD)

THAT'S IT! THE TIME HAS COME...

IS EVERYTHING ALL RIGHT, DARREN, I HEARD A...

NGH...

A GREAT HAIRY MONSTER...

WHAT IS IT, DEB-BIE!?

AAAAAH!!!

MON-STER...?

!!!

OH NO... NOT NOW!

IT'S OKAY...

IT'S DARREN.

THIS IS MY SECOND PHASE, WHICH MEANS THAT IN A FEW WEEKS, I'LL BE A FULL-VAMPIRE.

THE VAMPIRE BLOOD IN MY VEINS IS FINALLY REPLACING MY HUMAN CELLS WITH VAMPIRE CELLS.

THE PURGE?

THANKS...

I'LL GET SOME WATER AND A TOWEL.

WHAT'S SO BAD ABOUT IT?

IT'S TER-RIBLE TIMING...

BUT YOU'LL BE A FULL-VAMPIRE, RIGHT? YOU DON'T SOUND TOO HAPPY ABOUT IT.

IF WE GET INTO A FIGHT WITH THE VAMPANEZE, I CAN'T BE COUNTED ON...

I DON'T KNOW WHAT MY BODY'S GOING TO DO FROM ONE MINUTE TO THE NEXT.

MY HEAD'S POUNDING. I CAN'T SEE, HEAR, OR SMELL RIGHT.

I'M VULNER-ABLE.

IT NEVER FELT RIGHT TO BE A HALF-VAMPIRE PRINCE.

IT'S BEEN EIGHTEEN YEARS SINCE MR. CREPSLEY BLOODED ME...

IN MANY WAYS I'M GLAD—I'LL FINALLY BE A TRUE VAMPIRE.

ON THE OTHER HAND, I'M FACING THE END OF A WAY OF LIFE.

NOW I HAVE TO LEAVE THE WORLD OF LIGHT BEHIND FOREVER, SKULKING IN THE DARKNESS FOR THE REST OF MY DAYS.

NO MORE SUNLIGHT OR BEING ABLE TO PASS FOR HUMAN.

ALL DONE!

BASA (FLAP)

THANKS, THAT'S MUCH BETTER.

HEE!

NOPE.

STILL GOT WHIS-KERS?

LOOK ...

YOU'RE ALREADY GROWING.

HA HA HA.

YOU'RE RIGHT ...

JUST YESTER-DAY, I WAS TALLER THAN YOU!

I SEE...AN ADULT...

SO WHEN THE PURGE IS OVER, YOU'LL BE AN ADULT IN THE END?

YEAH... WEIRD, HUH?

I'VE BEEN A CHILD OR TEENAGER FOR THE BETTER PART OF THIRTY YEARS... AND NOW I'LL BE AN ADULT.

ERR, YES...

DO YOU REMEMBER WHEN YOU TRIED TO KISS ME A FEW YEARS AGO?

RIGHTLY SO. AS A TEACHER, IT WOULD BE WRONG OF ME TO GET INVOLVED WITH A CHILD.

WE WERE TEACHER AND STUDENT. YOU HIT THE ROOF AND ORDERED ME OUT OF YOUR APARTMENT.

IN A FEW WEEKS, YOU WON'T BE A BOY.

IT DOES?

BUT THAT ENDS IN A FEW WEEKS.

YOU CAN BE SO DENSE.

OH, DARREN...

YOU'LL
BE A
MAN.

OH...

I GUESS
IT'S NOT...
ALL BAD.

GUGU
(STRAIN)

BA
(CHOP)

ONCE THIS AGGRAVATING HEADACHE AND MY OUT-OF-CONTROL SENSES CALM DOWN...

GOOD. NO MORE PAIN...

THAT VOICE!

KIIN
(RING)

BIRI
(RIIIP)

HO, THERE!! IT'S BEEN A WHILE, FRIENDS!!!

VANCHA!!!

DARREN! I'VE MISSED YOU!!!

I COULDN'T GET HERE FAST ENOUGH!!!

I HEARD OUR OLD PALS MORGAN AND R.V. SHOWED UP!!

HE TOLD YOU WE WOULD HAVE FOUR CHANCES TO KILL LEONARD, AYE? THEN MAYBE WE BOTH HAVE TO BE THERE.

BUT I HAVE TO ADMIT, DES TINY DOESN'T MAKE MANY MISTAKES WHEN IT COMES TO PROPHE-CIES.

MAYBE MR. TINY GOT IT WRONG.

WHEN HE HAD ME AT HIS MERCY RECENTLY, THAT WAS OUR FOURTH EN-COUNTER, YET WE'RE BOTH STILL ALIVE.

I SEE. SO STEVE AND GANNEN ARE HERE TOO...

THEY COULD ATTACK AT ANY TIME.

STEVE WILL KNOW WHERE TO FIND THE CIRQUE, THANKS TO DARIUS.

THEY'RE GOING TO PULL ANOTHER STUNT HERE IN THIS TOWN, THAT'S FOR CERTAIN.

I WANT TO HEAR HIBERNIUS'S OPINION. THE CIRQUE IS IN TOWN, IS IT NOT?

CAN'T GO WANDERING AROUND WITH THE HEAVY POLICE PRESENCE.

THEN WE'LL GIVE YOU A RIDE.

YES. PERHAPS WE SHOULD RETURN TO... DISCUSS OUR PLANS.

BATAN (THUMP)

THANKS FOR THE ADVICE!

TRY NOT TO GET YOURSELF SHOT THIS TIME, DARREN!

WILL DO!

CALL IF YOU HAVE ANYTHING TO REPORT.

OF US ALL, ONLY VANCHA SENSED SOMETHING AMONG US THAT DAY...

YOU'RE IMAGINING THINGS. WE'RE OFF FOR THE CIRQUE DU FREAK!

WHAT'S WRONG, VANCHA?

I CAN'T HELP BUT FEEL AS THOUGH SOMEONE'S WATCHING US...

MOZOZO (RUSTLE)

...BUT BEGGARS CAN'T BE CHOOSERS.

THIS AIN'T MY STYLE...

?

...ITS ETERNAL GAZE PASSING FROM ONE TO THE OTHER...

...THE PRESENCE OF DEATH.

VANCHA...

OF COURSE HE IS. HARKAT IS WITH HIM NOW.

RIGHT, MR. TALL?

I SURE HOPE DARREN IS SAFE...

...AND ONE OTHER MAN...

SIGH...

WOW...I THINK THAT MIGHT BE THE FIRST TIME I'VE EVER SEEN MR. TALL NOT PAYING ATTENTION.

...

!

MR. TALL?

...MM? AH, YES...

PARDON ME...MUST BE GOING BACK TO MY TRAILER...

THIS MOMENT SHOULD NOT BE UPON US YET...

IT IS TOO SOON...

MOZO

MOZOZO (RUSTLE)

ALAS, OUR TIME IS RUNNING OUT...

CHAPTER 101:
MR. TALL'S PROPHECY

SHANCUS!!

HEY, TAKE IT EASY...MY EARS ARE SENSITIVE.

GOD- FATHER! MY GOD- FATHER!

WELCOME, EVERYONE!

GERA (CHA)

GERA

GERA

THAT'S SO WEIRD!

...!!!

WHY ?

WHY ?

HUH? HOW COME? DO THEY HURT? WHY?

YOUR SECOND PURGE!?

GAYA

GAYA (MURMUR)

HEY! HAVE YOU CHANGED?

WE WERE WORRIED, DARREN. WE HEARD YOU WERE SHOT...

...?

OUCH...

WOW, COOL! HE'S GOT A SCAR!!!

I SEE... NO WONDER YOU SEEM DIFFERENT...

AND ME!!

ME TOO!!

I WANNA BE BIG AND TOUGH TOO! THEN I'LL FIGHT THE VAMPANEZE!!

AWWW! DARREN GETS ALL THE FUN ADVENTURES!!

HA HA...

HE NEVER TOLD YOU? AND YOU... NEVER NOTICED?

YOUR SECOND PURGE!!

...COMING AT THE WORST POSSIBLE TIME.

IT'S A HAPPY DAY...

I'M NOT THE ONLY ONE. WE'VE ALL BEEN EDGY HERE LATELY.

I'VE FELT EYES ON MY BACK A FEW TIMES RECENTLY, LATE AT NIGHT WHEN I'VE BEEN WANDERING AROUND.

I CAN HANDLE IT!

YOU WANT TO BE SHOT BY BOW-GUNS?

YOU DON'T LIKE GETTING HURT, DO YOU?

FOL-LOWED?

SORRY, DARREN. I WANTED TO VISIT...

...BUT HIBERNIUS SAID I MIGHT BE FOLLOWED.

TOO LATE NOW...

WE NEED TO EXPLAIN THINGS... AND MOVE THE CIRQUE!

IT MUST BE... THE VAMPA-NEZE.

KOKU (NOD)

LET'S GO SEE WHAT HIBERNIUS HAS TO SAY.

VANCHA, DARREN, HARKAT, COME IN.

I HAVE BEEN EXPECTING YOU.

MR. TALL? IT'S ME, DARREN.

DEBBIE, ALICE, YOU TOO.

GACHA
(CLICK)

ZOKU~
(SHIVER)

I HOPE YOU DO NOT THINK ME RUDE FOR NOT VISITING...

...AND I HAD MUCH TO PUT IN ORDER HERE.

I KNEW YOU WOULD RECOV- ER...

...THAT'S OKAY...

TELL US WHERE WE CAN FIND STEVE LEONARD.

LET'S GET RIGHT DOWN TO BUSINESS.

I CANNOT. BUT REST ASSURED, HE WILL MAKE HIMSELF KNOWN SOON.

WHEN DOES HE PLAN TO STRIKE? WHERE!?

DOES THAT MEAN HE'S GOING TO ATTACK? IS HE NEARBY?

GIRO
(GLARE)

IT IS MUCH
HARDER TO
STAND BACK
AND WATCH
PASSIVELY.
HARDER THAN
YOU COULD
EVER IMAGINE.

IF YOU HAVE
THE POWER
TO SEE INTO
THE FUTURE,
THEN YOU
SHOULD
USE IT FOR
GOOD!

YOU KNEW
WHO THE
ENEMY WAS
AND THAT
LARTEN
WOULD DIE!

YOU KNEW
WHAT
WOULD
HAPPEN IN
THE
STADIUM
AND EVERY-
THING
ELSE!

...EVER
SINCE
GLIMPSING
HIS
PROBABLE
DEATH.

YOU WEPT
FOR LARTEN
WHEN HE
DIED—BUT
I GRIEVED
FOR HIM
FOR THIRTY
YEARS IN
ADVANCE...

VERY
WELL,
HIBER-
NIUS...

...

WAIT.

LET'S
GO.

YOU DON'T KNOW?

DARREN, YOU CAN'T...

AND WHAT OF OUR FINAL ENCOUNTER?

WHO WILL DIE? WILL WE WIN OR LOSE?

WHAT PROFIT WOULD THERE BE IN KNOWING?

WHY...?

NOT EVEN MR. TINY KNOWS THE OUTCOME OF THIS BATTLE.

THERE ARE TWO DISTINCT POTENTIAL FUTURES.

...AND LISTENED TO THE SCREAMS OF THOSE WHO'LL PERISH IF WE FAIL.

FOR TWO YEARS I'VE DREAMT OF THE DESTRUCTION OF THE CLAN...

AND THE VISIONS ONLY GROW MORE AND MORE VIVID...

IF WE SHOULD LOSE, I WANT TO KNOW...

...WHETHER VANCHA OR I WILL DIE.

SHE ALSO SAID THAT IF THE VAMPIRES WERE TO LOSE, ONLY ONE OF THE HUNTERS WOULD REMAIN TO SEE THE EXTINCTION OF OUR PEOPLE...

EVANNA SAID THE SAME THING.

DOKKA (FWUMP)

TCH! FINE, THEN! TELL US, HIBERNIUS!!

IF YOU DON'T KNOW WHETHER WE WIN OR LOSE, YOU CAN STILL LOOK INTO THE FUTURE IN WHICH WE'VE LOST!

I HAVE TO KNOW.

I'M SORRY, VANCHA...

DAR-REN! YOU CAN'T JUST—

IT IS ONLY PAIN THAT LOOKING INTO THE FUTURE BRINGS...

IT IS BETTER NOT TO KNOW THE FATE OF LOVED ONES AND FRIENDS.

...

VERY WELL...

I STILL WANT TO KNOW...

AS YOU DESIRE...

...I WILL CAST MY EYES A NUMBER OF DECADES FORWARD...

CREAKSHOW

SULIII (SWOOSH)

RYU!!!

HE'S GLOWING RED...

PASHI (CRAK)

PARI (CRIK)

IT'S COLD!!

BURU (SHIVER)

FFFH...

... THOSE OF VAMPIRES AND VAMPANEZE.

I LOOKED INTO BOTH FUTURES ...

AND?

I HAVE LOOKED ...

IN THE FUTURE WHERE THE VAMPIRES WON, I FOUND DARREN.

IN NEITHER FUTURE ...

...DID I FIND VANCHA.

BUT ...

THE LORD OF THE SHADOWS IS DESTINED TO DESTROY YOU, VANCHA.

IS THAT... STEVE'S TITLE?

WHO'S THIS LORD OF THE SHADOWS?

NO...

...

THAT CAN'T BE... IF VANCHA IS KILLED BY THE LORD OF THE SHADOWS...

...THEN IF THE VAMPIRES WIN, I'M GOING TO KILL HIM?

CALM DOWN, DARREN.

IN BOTH FUTURES? THAT CAN'T BE! LOOK AGAIN!

SO I'LL DIE WHETHER WE WIN OR LOSE.

HAH. I'VE BEEN READY FOR THAT.

HE MIGHT BE STEVE LEONARD, AND HE MIGHT NOT.

THE LORD OF THE SHADOWS IS THE CRUEL LEADER WHO WILL RUIN THE WORLD AFTER THE WAR OF THE SCARS.

SO IT IS THE FIRST TIME YOU HAVE HEARD THE TERM?

HE WILL SEIZE THE REINS OF POWER OVER THE EARTH FROM MANKIND AND DESTROY ALL THAT LIVES.

NO MATTER WHAT HAPPENS IN THE WAR OF THE SCARS, THE LORD OF THE SHADOWS WILL ARISE.

AND IN THE OTHER...

...THE LORD OF THE SHADOWS IS ME.

IN ONE, THE VAMPANEZE LORD HAS BECOME THE MASTER OF SHADOWS AND RULER OF THE DARK.

TWO STRONG FUTURES LIE AHEAD OF YOU.

EVANNA MADE THE PROPHECY JUST FOR ME.

THE ONLY QUESTION IS WHO WILL BE THE LORD OF THE SHADOWS.

WHAT DO YOU MEAN? EVEN IF WE KILL STEVE...

...THE FUTURE WILL STILL BE THAT... WASTE-WORLD WE FOUND?

HE IS UPON US.

WITHIN TWENTY-FOUR HOURS, HE WILL BE BORN.

GAAN (BOOM)

AAAAH!

THE WAR OF THE SCARS IS SOON TO REACH ITS END.

THERE IS NO TURNING BACK.

THEY ARE HERE. PREPARE YOURSELVES.

THAT WAS A GUNSHOT!

NOT ALL OF THE SIX OF US WILL SURVIVE THE NIGHT...

EVRA!!

NO! DON'T YOU DARE TOUCH SHAN-CUS!!

BACK OFF! THAT'S MY SNAKE!

STOP IT!! LET ME GO!!!

I'D SHTAY NISHE AHN QUIEH UHF I WHUUH YOU...

HEH-HEH-HEH! CAUGHT ME A SNAKE-BOY!

I WONDER WHAT KINDA SOUNDS HE'LL MAKE IF I START PEEL-ING OFF THOSE SCALES?

CHAPTER 102: FATHER AND SON

DAR-REN!!

SHI-LENSHE!!

DON'T HURT MY BABY!!

NO! LET SHAN-CUS GO!

HEE-HEE, THE SNAKE-BOY'S MINE!!

LET GO OF ME!!

JA (CLICK)

ZUKI (THROB)

ZUKI

NOT ALL OF THE SIX OF US WILL SURVIVE THE NIGHT ...

YOU DON'T WANT TO MISS YOUR TARGET ...

OH-OH!

DAMN!

134

IF YOU GET IN OUR WAY, HE DIES.

STUFF IT, SHAN. WE'RE TAKING THE BOY.

TAKE ME INSTEAD. I'LL SWAP FOR SHANCUS.

YOU CAN'T GET OUT OF HERE, R.V.

GROSS!!

EUGH!

ZUGU (WINCE)

I WANNA HEAR THE MELODIES OF HIS SCREAMS AS I PLUCK OFF HIS SCALES.

NOT ANOTHER STEP, OR I'LL...

STAY BACK.

I CANNOT ALLOW THIS.

ZUI (LOOM)

I SAID, DON'T MOVE!

ONE STEP?

SU (SWISH)

OR
...

THAT
WAS
HALF
A
STEP.

...
I'LL
...

KACHI
(CLICK)

GAAN
(BLAM)

SU (SWISH)

IT'S TOO LATE FOR HIM.

WHAT ARE YOU DOING? WE HAVE TO SAVE HIM!

DA! (LEAP)

MR. TALL...

THIS... CAN'T BE...

MR. TINY! EVANNA!

WHY? WHY DID YOU DO THIS?

YOU COULD HAVE KILLED MORGAN RATHER THAN TAKING THE BULLET.

...MY TIME REMAINING WAS SHORT...

PLUS... YOU MUST HAVE KNOWN THAT...

THIS IS MY FORTRESS... THESE ARE MY PEOPLE...

NGH...

LEAVING IT TO STRIKE EVRA DOWN? I THINK NOT...

...MAY YOU BE TRIUMPHANT...

EVEN IN DEATH...

"JIWA (SEP)"

FUU-CFFHH)

I WILL REMEMBER YOU...

GOODBYE, SISTER...

THANK YOU, FATHER...

MR. TINY AND MR. TALL...ARE FATHER AND SON!?!

GA
(STOMP)

ALAS...

NO AMOUNT OF MAGIC WILL SAVE YOU FROM BEING SHOT DEAD...

MY SON IS DEAD.

...THE KILLERS WILL ESCAPE WITH THE YOUNG VON BOY.

DARREN! IF YOU WASTE TIME PICKING A FIGHT WITH MY FATHER...

HEY! DON'T DO THAT!

DARREN, HARKAT, AND DEBBIE, TAKE MORGAN AND THE BOY!

ALICE AND EVRA WITH ME. WE'LL GO AFTER R.V. AND SHANCUS!

I'M COMING TOO.

WE HAVE TO CHASE THEM!

...BUT YOU'RE NOT QUITE THERE YET, DARREN.

IT'S A VERY GOOD COLOR...

YOU NEED TO BE DARKER... MORE RED...

THERE THEY ARE! IT'S MORGAN AND DARIUS!

DON'T CHARGE AHEAD, DARREN! CAREFUL!

TCH! AW-RUDDY CUHT UP TAH USH!?

DAAN (BLAM)

AAAAGH!!!

TOO BAHD...

JUSH LYKE MY LOHD SHAID... SHTUCK IN THUH PUHGE...

LYKE IHT?

UH'M GONNA DUH THE SHAHM TUH YUH!

DO.
(THUD)

HAA

HAA
(HUFF)

GAHA
(GAHHK)

AH...

AHH!

GORO
(ROLL)

GA
(GRAB)

BISHU
(BZIPP)

S-STAY
BACK!

DAN
(THUNGG)

ZUGU
(THROB)

ZUGU

HE'S JUST A CHILD!!

DARREN, NO!

YOU'LL BECOME A MONSTER IF YOU KILL THAT BOY!

YOU'LL BE NO BETTER THAN STEVE!

DARREN...

HE'S A LITTLE BOY!

NO! HE'S STEVE LEONARD'S SON!

EVERY VAMPANEZE MUST DIE.

EVERY VAMPET!

ZUKI (THROB)

ZUKI

I KNOW ALL ABOUT YOU, SO STOP PRETENDING YOU GIVE A DAMN!!

GO AHEAD AND KILL ME! IT'S WHAT YOUR KIND DOES! YOU'RE MURDERERS!

WHO CARES? THIS IS YOUR BEST CHANCE!

BUT MR. CREPSLEY SAID...

LIVE AS A FREE VAMPIRE, NOT AS A TWISTED, REVENGE-DRIVEN CREATURE OF DESPAIR.

WHO KILLED MR. CREPSLEY, TOMMY, AND MR. TALL!?

NO, DON'T KILL HIM...

LOOK IN HIS EYES—HE'S TERRIFIED!

GWAAH!!!

KILL HIM!!

KILL HIM!!!

GET REVENGE!!!

ZUKI

ZUKI

CHAPTER 103: THE PATH OF FATE

NOW YOU'LL KNOW...

...THE PAIN I FELT!!!

DARREN!!!

WHAT BETTER WAY THAN TO KILL HIS OWN SON!?

STEVE NEEDS TO UNDERSTAND THE FEELING OF THE DEATH OF HIS LOVED ONES!

DEB-BIE...

DO YOU UNDER-STAND ME, DARREN?

YOU NEED TO BEAT STEVE IN THE WAY ONLY YOU CAN.

IF DEBBIE HADN'T STOPPED ME...

...I'D HAVE...

HENA ^*^

HENA (SHIVER) ^*^

THANKS, HAR-KAT.

HERE, WE SHOULD STOP... THE BLEED-ING.

...

ALICE?

I'LL AN-SWER IT.

THANK YOU.

V V V...

VANCHA SAYS HE THINKS... HE CAN KILL R.V. NOW, IF NEED BE...

THEY'VE FOUND R.V. AND SHANCUS... AND ARE IN PURSUIT.

OKAY, I SEE...

...

YES, MORGAN'S DEAD.

...

...

...BUT HE THINKS R.V.... MIGHT BE LEADING US TO STEVE.

SHOULD WE KILL R.V. NOW, OR FOLLOW HIM?

VANCHA WANTS DARREN... TO DECIDE.

WHAT DOES EVRA SAY?

NO! IF ANYTHING, WE SHOULD BE TRYING TO SAVE SHANCUS!

SU... (SSK)

EVRA IS ONLY THINKING...OF SHANCUS.

BUT WE HAVE TO CONSIDER MORE THAN THAT.

KEEP TRAILING R.V. TO WHEREVER HE'S HEADED.

PASS THE MESSAGE TO VANCHA.

I'M GOING WITH YOU.

NO.

YOU GO BACK TO THE CIRQUE DU FREAK AND HAVE SOMEONE LOOK AT YOUR HAND, DEBBIE.

SFX: GYU (SQUEEZE)

WE CAN USE HIM TO STRIKE A DEAL WITH STEVE.

WE'RE TAKING DARIUS WITH US.

DAR-REN!!

HOW LONG HAVE YOU BEEN WATCHING US?

EVAN-NA...

PIKU (TWITCH)

I WILL JOIN HIM AGAIN PRESENTLY...

WHY AREN'T YOU WITH YOUR FATHER?

YOU KNEW I WAS HERE?

DARREN AND I HAVE SOMETHING TO DISCUSS.

WILL YOU TAKE DARIUS AND GO ON AHEAD?

HARKAT, DEBBIE, FORGIVE ME.

...

LET'S GO, DEBBIE.

WE WILL COME AFTER YOU SOON.

I KNOW WHERE TO GO.

...NOW... DO YOU HAVE SOMETHING TO ASK ME?

NO! I DO.

...I SEE.

SO I WAS WRONG.

...

ASK AWAY, THEN.

INDEED?

...IS IT CERTAIN THAT I WILL FILL THAT ROLE?

IF WE ARE TRIUMPHANT IN THE WAR OF THE SCARS...

IT'S ABOUT...

...THE LORD OF THE SHADOWS.

GU (SQUEEZE)

AND IT WILL HAPPEN WITHIN THE NEXT TWENTY-FOUR HOURS.

IT IS.

ZUKI (THROB)

ZUKI

IT CAN'T HAPPEN...

IT'S IMPOSSIBLE...

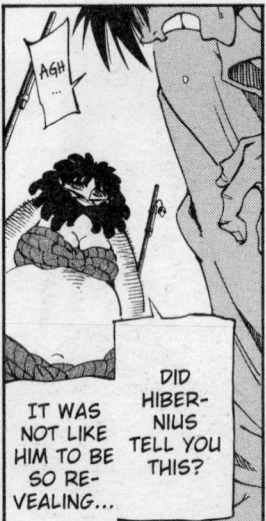

AGH...

IT WAS NOT LIKE HIM TO BE SO RE-VEALING...

DID HIBERNIUS TELL YOU THIS?

GIRI (GRIT)

NO! YOU'RE WRONG! YOU AND MR. TALL!

I WOULDN'T HURT VANCHA... OR MY FRIENDS!!!

...HATRED THAT WILL CONSUME YOU.

YOU ARE FILLING WITH HATRED, DARREN...

THEY GROW, THEY MATURE, THEY BECOME.

MONSTERS ARE NOT BORN FULLY DEVELOPED.

ULU (SOB)

ULU (SOB)

SHE PULLED YOU BACK FROM THE BRINK.

IT IS FORTUNATE FOR YOU THAT DEBBIE WAS THERE.

...IS NO LONGER JUST THE EFFECT OF YOUR VAMPIRIC PURGE.

ZUGU

ZUGU (THROBB)

YOUR TERRIBLE HEAD-ACHE...

YOU WILL DESTROY THE VAMPANEZE, BUT THAT WON'T BE ENOUGH. THERE WILL ALWAYS BE A NEW ENEMY TO FIGHT.

DURING YOUR QUEST, CERTAIN VAMPIRES WILL TRY TO STOP YOU. THEY TOO WILL DIE AT YOUR HANDS. EVEN HUMANS...

STEVE WILL LEAD THE VAMPANEZE TO VICTORY...

YOU CAN LEAD A PEACEFUL LIFE—UNTIL HE BRINGS THE WORLD CRASHING DOWN AROUND YOU, OF COURSE.

...THEN WHAT IS THE POINT OF THIS WAR?

BUT IF THE LORD OF THE SHADOWS IS DESTINED TO COME FORTH AND DESTROY THE WORLD, REGARDLESS OF WHO WINS...

THERE MUST BE!

THERE MUST BE SOME WAY TO AVOID IT!

YES, I KNOW.

BUT...I CAN'T DO THAT.

LEAVE YOUR FRIENDS. HIDE.

BURU (SHIVER)

ブル

ブル

GO. WALK AWAY.

...EITHER DEATH BY STEVE'S HAND, OR A RISE TO INFAMY AS THE LORD OF THE SHADOWS.

EVEN THOUGH YOU HAVE THE BEST WILL IN THE WORLD, YOU'LL SEE DESTINY THROUGH TO ITS BITTER END...

THAT IS WHY YOU CANNOT ESCAPE.

...AND IT WOULD NOT DO TO MISS A MOMENT MORE OF IT.

THIS NIGHT IS CENTRAL TO THE FUTURE...

NOW, LET US HURRY AFTER YOUR FRIENDS.

STEVE...

I SEE... SO THIS IS YOUR GAME.

THIS IS THE PLACE WHERE IT ALL BEGAN...

...OR HINDER?

ARE YOU HERE TO HELP, MY LADY...

HURM!

NEITHER, MY PRINCE. I SERVE MERELY AS A WITNESS.

HE'S GONNA KILL ALL OF YOU!!!

MY DAD'S GONNA GET YOU MURDEROUS VAMPIRES! YOU'LL PAY FOR USING ALL THOSE HUMANS FOR FOOD!!

BURU BURU (SHIVER)

DON'T WORRY, EVRA. WE'LL GET SHANCUS BACK, SAFE AND SOUND.

YOU SHUT UP ABOUT MY DAD!

OH, BE QUIET.

STEVE'S FED HIM A LOAD OF NONSENSE ABOUT US.

I KNOW YOU WILL. YOU SAVED ME WHEN MURLOUGH GOT HIS UGLY MITTS ON ME.

FORGET IT. THERE'S NO USE TALKING TO THE BRAT.

AND THEN...

...THE DOOR LEADING TO THE STAGE.

...STEVE AND I, TICKETS CLUTCHED IN OUR HANDS.

THE HALL WE WALKED DOWN...

THE GROOVES FROM MR. TALL'S HAT...

THE CEILING FEELS CLOSER THAN IT DID THAT DAY.

YOU CAN'T LET CONCERN FOR SHANCUS OVERRIDE ALL.

...BUT THE LIVES OF EVERYONE ELSE HERE IN ORDER TO STOP STEVE.

WE HAVE TO BE READY TO SACRIFICE NOT JUST OURSELVES...

STEEL YOURSELF, DARREN.

...RIGHT THROUGH THESE DOORS...

GIII (CREAK)

STEVE'S AHEAD...

IT'S PITCH BLACK.

GI
(CREAK)

DARREN!!!

!!!!

BA
(FLASH)

...AND I, LORD OF THE VAMPANEZE AND MASTER OF CEREMONIES.

...R.V., THE MADMAN WHO CLAIMS HIS "V" STANDS FOR "VAMPANEZE," A TERRIFIED LITTLE SNAKE-BOY...

TONIGHT'S PERFORMANCE WILL BE BROUGHT TO YOU BY GANNEN HARST, OUR RIGHT-HAND MAN...

SHAN-CUS!!!!

SHAN-CUS!!!

HYUUU (WHISTLE)

DAN (WHAM)

DAN

KA (THOKK)

IS THAT YOU, DARIUS? SO YOU'RE ALIVE.

I DON'T SEE MORGAN WITH YOU... OH WELL.

KUKU CHEH

DAD !!!

CARE TO TRY AGAIN? HA-HA!

BAD LUCK, SIRE!

A TREATY!? LUDICROUS!

I'D LIKE TO DISCUSS A PEACE TREATY!

I WANT TO CHAT, DARREN.

THAT WILL REQUIRE ...

ALAS, OUR PEACE TALKS SEEM TO HAVE BROKEN DOWN. THAT MEANS THE TIME OF FINAL RECKONING IS NIGH.

NIYA

NIYA (SMIRK)

...

MAYBE YOU WANT TO BECOME MY BLOOD-BROTHER.

HA!

IN A WAY, I ALREADY AM.

IN THE OLD DAYS, A SACRIFICE WAS ALWAYS MADE BEFORE A LARGE BATTLE, TO APPEASE THE GODS.

...A SACRIFICE.

SO LET'S SACRIFICE THIS LITTLE SNAKE-BOY FOR DIVINE FAVOR!

LET HIM GO!! SHANCUS!!!

DON'T YOU DARE TOUCH HIM!!

I HAVE...

...NO SAY IN IT, BROTHER...

I KNOW YOU CAN HEAR ME, GANNEN!

GANNEN! YOU CAN'T ALLOW THIS!

GO ON, R.V.

I'M NOT SURE ABOUT THIS, MAN... HE'S JUST A KID.

D... DAD?

NOW, YOU BEARDED, ARMLESS FREAK— ARE YOU READY?

MMM! MMM!

DON'T DISOBEY ME! I MADE YOU, AND I CAN BREAK YOU!

HE'S JUST A KID...LIKE ME.

YOU CAN'T—

YOU'RE NOT REALLY GOING TO KILL HIM...ARE YOU?

DAAAAD!!!

SHANCUS!!

PUHA (BWAAH)

BE QUIET. YOU DON'T UNDER- STAND WHAT'S HAPPEN- ING.

BUT...

SHUT UP!!!

BIKU (TWITCH)

THAT'S RIGHT! WE WILL!

WE'RE COMING FOR YOU, SHANCUS!!

I KNOW YOU AND DARREN WILL SAVE ME!

I'M NOT AFRAID! I'M FINE!

LET GO, YOU BIG MONSTER!!

GABU (CHOMP)

LET GO!!

I AIN'T NO MONSTER...

I CAN KILL ADULTS... BUT NOT KIDS, MAN.

I...I CAN'T DO THIS...

R.V.!!

SHANCUS!!!

KILL HIM, R.V.!!!

I CAN'T...

D... DAD...

AHH ...

VERY WELL.

DAR-REN ...

THROW AWAY YOUR WEAPONS AND WE'LL SWAP THE TWO BOYS.

DO IT, BEFORE I CHANGE MY MIND.

A-ARE YOU SURE, STEVE ?

WE WON'T ATTACK IF YOU DON'T.

GO GET THE PLANK AND EX-TEND IT ACROSS THE PIT.

...

YOU'RE NOT AS BAD AS YOU LOOK, MISTER.

...

GOOD ...

HAA. (SIGH)

LET'S HEAR HIM OUT...

HE'S TIED, JUST LIKE WE ARE. HE WON'T RISK HIS SON'S LIFE.

THINK WE CAN TRUST HIM?

ZURU

ZURU
(DRAG)

HURRY! PASS THE PLANK OVER!

WAIT, DARREN.

DARE GAMES.

REMEMBER THE GAMES WE PLAYED WHEN WE WERE CHILDREN?

ONE OF US WOULD STICK HIS HAND IN A FIRE OR JAB A PIN IN HIS LEG.

THEN HE'D TURN TO THE OTHER...

...AND SAY, "I DARE YOU TO DO THIS."

...NO MATTER WHAT HAPPENS BETWEEN US...

HEY, DAR-REN...

TELL ME...

HEY, DARREN!

NO. EVEN STEVE WOULDN'T...

STEVE? YOU CAN'T...

MY LORD!!

HOW COULD YOU...

NO, DAD...

BASTARD!!

I DARE YOU!! I DOUBLE DARE YOU!!!

GO ON, DARREN!!! SHOW ME YOU CAN DO IT!!!

HE NEEDS ME TO MATCH HIS EVIL DEEDS.

IT'S ALL CLEAR NOW.

YES, STEVE... I UNDERSTAND YOU.

DO IT, DARREN! KILL DARIUS!!

IF I KILL DARIUS, HE CAN JUSTIFY HIS CRUELTY AND CONTINUE.

DON'T LEAVE ME AS THE ONLY VILLAIN HERE!!

DARIUS, TELL DARREN YOUR MOTHER'S NAME!!

BOO... (WHUFF?)

BE CAREFUL, DARREN! YOU DON'T KNOW WHO YOU'RE KILLING!!

PIKU (TWITCH)

TELL HIM YOUR MOTHER'S NAME!! NOW!!!

HE'S ABOUT TO DRIVE A KNIFE THROUGH YOUR HEART!!

A...

ANNIE ...

BURU (SHIVER)

BURU

WHAT... DID YOU SAY?

ANNIE... SHAN... WHAT ABOUT IT?

YOU SEE, DAR- REN...

...IF YOU KILL DARIUS, YOU WON'T JUST BE SLAUGH- TERING MY SON.

YOU'LL BE MUR- DERING YOUR NEPHEW!

DARIUS IS MY AND ANNIE'S SON.

THERE IS NO STORY
WITHOUT AN END...

AND THUS, THE CIRQUE DU FREAK SERIES
WILL REACH ITS CONCLUSION IN VOLUME
TWELVE, "SONS OF DESTINY"...

LORD OF THE SHADOWS · END

A QUICK GUIDE TO THE STORY OF THE DARREN SHAN MANGA VERSION (SORT OF)!!

PART II!!!!!!!!!

in USA

ANYWAY...

I MEAN, I'D ALWAYS HOPED I WOULD GET THE CHANCE TO VISIT THERE, BUT WHO KNEW IT WOULD COME THIS WAY?

HEH HEH!

WHAT THIS "IN THE USA" PART MEANS?

OH, CAN YOU GUESS WHAT'S COMING?

I GOT THE CHANCE TO VISIT AMERICA AS PART OF A STRATEGY TO HELP CROSS-PROMOTE THE MOVIE IN JAPAN THROUGH THIS MANGA EDITION!!

HOW DID THIS DREAM COME TRUE? THROUGH THE HELP OF TOHO TOWA CO., LTD.!

WE'RE NOT WORTHY...

MATSUOKA-SAN, ITSUKI-SAN, THANK YOU SO MUCH!!!

SFX: KIRA (SPARKLE) KIRA KIRA

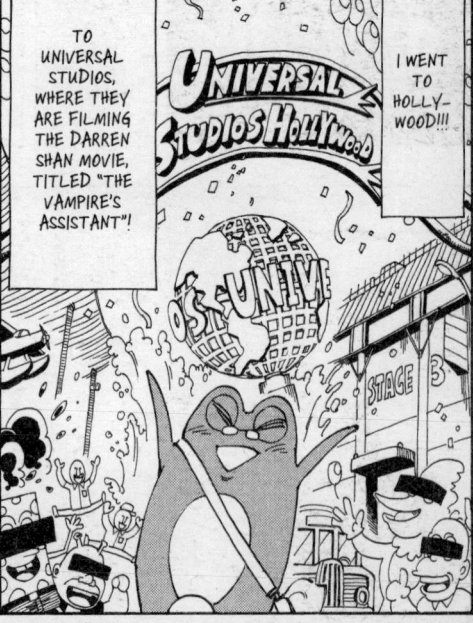

TO UNIVERSAL STUDIOS, WHERE THEY ARE FILMING THE DARREN SHAN MOVIE, TITLED "THE VAMPIRE'S ASSISTANT"!

I WENT TO HOLLY-WOOD!!!

SO WITH THAT, LET'S TAKE A VISIT TO DIRECTOR PAUL WEITZ'S STUDIO!

ZORO

ZORO (TROMP)

DOKI

DOKI (BA-BLUMP)

TODAY I'M GETTING THE CHANCE TO VIEW A PRE-EDITED PILOT VERSION OF THE FILM.

I FORGOT MY PASSPORT...

...

THEY TAKE THEIR SECURITY SERIOUSLY.

GO ON.

I'LL NEED TO SHOW MY PASSPORT FOR ID TO GET INTO THE STUDIO.

SFX: GOSO (RUSTLE) GOSO

HANG ON. I KNOW I PUT IT IN HERE THIS MORNING...

HEY, BRO?

NOT UNTIL I SEE DARREN'S MOVIE!!

BUT I CAN'T DIE YET!

I MUST LIVE !!!...

GET IT TOGETHER, MAN...

TOBO (PLOD)

PAAN (THWACK)

TOBO

I SWEAR, I WANTED TO CRAWL INTO A HOLE AND DIE. WHY DID I COME TO AMERICA, ANYWAY?

DESPITE MISSING MY PASSPORT, I MANAGED TO CONVINCE THEM WHO I WAS TO GET IN...

HANDSOME GENTLEMAN! GREAT SMILE!

WATCHING THE FILM...

JIJI (BZZT)

AFTER THAT, WE GOT TO TALK DIRECTLY WITH DIRECTOR PAUL WEITZ-SAN!

GOOO (WHOOSH)

I MADE SURE TO ASK PLENTY OF QUESTIONS!!!

AND IN KEEPING WITH MY DUTY TO THE READERS!

WE HAD THE PERFECT THEATER TO SHOOT IN THERE. THE MOLD AND DUST WAS JUST RIGHT FOR THE LOOK OF THE SCENE.

WE SHOT THE FILM NOT IN ENGLAND, BUT NEW ORLEANS IN AMERICA.

DID YOU LIKE THE WAY WE DEPICTED FLITTING? HA HA! I LIKED THE ARTISTIC STYLING OF IT.

WHEN I READ THE BOOKS, I THOUGHT MR. TALL JUST HAD TO BE KEN WATANABE!

THE MOVIE'S BASED ON THE FIRST THREE VOLUMES OF THE STORY.

WILLEM DAFOE'S GAVNER WAS INCLUDED AS A TEASER FOR THE NEXT MOVIE! I HOPE I GET TO MAKE IT!

THE BOYS WHO PLAYED DARREN AND STEVE ARE SUPPOSED TO BE RIVALS, BUT THEY WERE BEST OF FRIENDS ON SET!

I CAN'T WAIT TO SEE HOW IT LOOKS WHEN IT'S DONE!

AND THIS WAS BEFORE ANY CG AND EFFECTS WERE ADDED!

IT WAS NOTHING SHORT OF MOVING TO SEE DARREN AND MR. CREPSLEY RUNNING ACROSS THE SCREEN!

うっとり... (SWOON)

うっとり...

THE MOVIE WAS SPLENDID! IT FULFILLED MY EVERY HOPE!

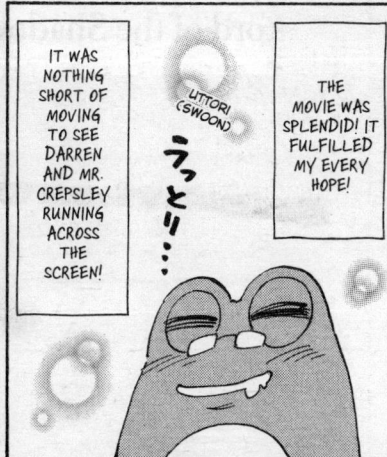

CHECK OUT THE MOVIE-ONLY CHARAC-TERS!

ONE OF THE CHARACTERS IN THE MOVIE WAS BASED ON A SKETCH PAUL DID AS A BOY!

PERSONALLY, I LOVED MR. TALL AND MR. TINY.

HE ALSO TOLD US ABOUT HIS FAVORITE LOCAL SHOP FOR COMIC BOOKS. ALL IN ALL, IT WAS AN INCREDIBLE EXPERIENCE.

THIS KIND OF THING NEVER HAPPENS! WE'RE SO LUCKY!

THANK YOU YOSHIKAWA-SAN, MY INTERPRETER!

AFTER THE INTERVIEW, PAUL-SAN ACTUALLY DROVE US AROUND THE STUDIO ON A CART!!

FOR MORE DETAILS ON THE MOVIE, CHECK OUT RECENT ISSUES OF SHONEN SUNDAY, WHERE YOU'LL FIND SOME MINI TRIP REPORT CARTOONS FROM ME. (JAPAN ONLY)

CIRQUE DU FREAK

"THE VAMPIRE'S ASSISTANT" HIT JAPAN IN 2009! BUT YOU CAN CHECK OUT THE DVD IN STORES NOW!!

SEE YOU NEXT TIME!!!

THE END

1 862684 21

T⬚⬚⬚⬚⬚⬚⬚⬚N ⑪
L

Darren Shan
Takahiro Arai

Translation: Stephen Paul
⬚⬚⬚⬚⬚⬚ Design
Art direction: Hitoshi SHIRAYAMA
Original cover design: Shigeru ANZAI + Bay Bridge Studio

Darren Shan Vol.11
Text © 2009 Darren Shan, Artworks © 2009 Takahiro ARAI
All rights reserved
Original Japanese edition published in Japan in 2009 by Shogakukan Inc., Tokyo.
Artwork reproduction rights in the UK and The Commonwealth arranged with
Shogakukan Inc. through Tuttle-Mori Agency, Inc., Tokyo.

English translation © 2011 Darren Shan

Published in Great Britain by HarperCollins *Children's Books* in 2012
HarperCollins *Children's Books* is a division of HarperCollins*Publishers* Ltd,
77–85 Fulham Palace Road, Hammersmith, London, W6 8JB.

The HarperCollins website address is
www.harpercollins.co.uk

ISBN: 978-0-00-750645-3

Printed and bound in England by Clays Ltd, St Ives plc

MIX
Paper from
responsible sources
FSC
www.fsc.org **FSC® C007454**

FSC™ is a non-profit international organisation established to promote the responsible
management of the world's forests. Products carrying the FSC label are independently
certified to assure consumers that they come from forests that are managed to meet
the social, economic and ecological needs of present and future generations, and other
controlled sources.

Find out more about HarperCollins and the environment at
www.harpercollins.co.uk/green